EGMONT
We bring stories to life

First published in Great Britain 2019 by Egmont UK Limited
The Yellow Building, 1 Nicholas Road, London W11 4AN

Illustrations by Gregory Sokol
Written by Katrina Pallant
Designed by Richie Hull

© & ™ 2019 Lucasfilm Ltd.
ISBN 978 1 4052 9289 4
70242/001
Printed in UK

To find more great *Star Wars* books, visit
www.egmont.co.uk/starwars

STAR WARS™

Joke Book

CONTENTS

HEEE

4

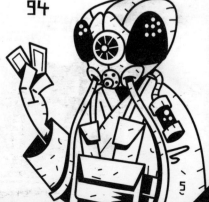

Why would Darth Vader never change a lightbulb?

He's a dark lord.

What goes "Ha ha ha-Aghhhhhh! Thump"?

A stormtrooper laughing at Darth Vader.

How many Sith Lords does it take to change a lightbulb?

Always two, there are. A Master and an Apprentice.

7

DARTH VADER

LOL!

What do Sith Lords have to wear on Dagobah?

Darth Waders.

What is Darth Vader's favourite food?

Sith kebab.

How does Darth Vader eat through his mask?

He's force-fed.

HAN SOLO

What do you call a smuggler who has been frozen in carbonite?

A hardened criminal.

Yoda hasn't been taking on any new students on Dagobah. He says he's swamped at work.

HA!

Why shouldn't you ask to borrow money from Yoda?

He's always a little short.

BAHAHA!

Why is the force like duct-tape?

It has a light side, a dark side, and it binds the galaxy together.

13

What car do Jedi Masters drive?

ToYodas.

What is a Jedi's favourite toy?

A yo-Yoda.

What did Yoda say to the librarian?

Due... or due not?

JEDI v. SITH

Why do doctors make the best Jedi?

Because a Jedi must have patience.

Why were the Jedi Master's eyes crossed?

He couldn't control his pupils.

Can Jedi Knights jump higher than a building?

Of course - buildings can't jump!

Where do Sith shop?

The Darth Mall.

JEDI V. SITH

A determined Padawan is studying the path of the Jedi. To prove his discipline, a vow of silence he takes. Two words, and two words only, he is allowed to speak, once every seven years. After seven years, the Jedi council summons him. His two words, they ask for.

"Very draughty," he says.

They nod and send him away. Seven more years pass, and back, for his next two words, he comes.

"Bad food," he says.

Again, they nod. Seven more years pass, and it is time again for his two words.

"I quit," he says.

"Surprised, I am not," the Grand Master says.

"You have done nothing but complain since you got here."

21

BOBA & JANGO

How did Boba Fett feel when he got a new jetpack?

Uplifted!

LOL!

What do you get if you mix a bounty hunter with a tropical fruit?

Mango Fett.

What is Jango's favourite pasta?

Fett-ucine.

What do you call a bounty hunter with money problems?

Boba Debt.

What's R2-D2 short for?

He's only got little legs.

Knock, knock.

Who's there?

Art.

Art who?

Artoo-Detoo!

What do you call the droid who's always getting lost?

R2-Dtour.

What do droids do at lunchtime?

They just have a quick byte.

How do droids say goodbye?

Microwaves.

Why was the battle droid acting funny?

He had a screw loose.

Why did the droid cross the road?

It was programmed by a chicken.

27

Did you hear about the violent Power Droid?

It was arrested for assault and battery.

K-250 is giving away his old batteries, if anyone wants them - free of charge.

A stormtrooper walks into a medical centre. He takes off his helmet and has a jogan fruit stuck in one ear, a nerf steak stuck in the other and a grape up his nose.

"I don't feel well," he says.

"I can see the problem," says the medical droid. "You're not eating properly."

Tarkin ordered a million camouflage uniforms for the troops, but now he can't find them.

???

Two snowtroopers are patrolling on Hoth and spot a huge wampa running towards them, so they start sprinting in the other direction.

One yells to the other, "You really think we can outrun that wampa?"

The other one says, "I don't have to ... I just have to outrun you!"

Two stormtroopers are searching Tatooine for some missing droids, and have run out of water. They climb a sand dune and spot a row of three tents on the other side.

There's a shopkeeper in the first tent, so they ask for water. "Sorry, no," he says, "all I have is sponge cake." That's not going to help, think the stormtroopers, so they try the second tent.

The shopkeeper in the second tent doesn't have any water either. "Sorry," he says, "all I've got is jelly and whipped cream." They can't drink that, so they head off to the third tent.

"Do you have any water?" they ask in the the third tent. "No," says the shopkeeper, "just these little multicoloured sprinkles."

The stormtroopers set off to find water, and one says to the other, "That was weird."
"Yes," says the other, "it was a trifle bazaar."

HEEE

32

Why don't Ewoks get told off for yelling?

Because they use their Endor voices.

What do you call an Ewok with no teeth?

A gummy bear.

How do Ewoks communicate over long distances?

With Ewokie-talkies.

35

Why couldn't the Empire find the rebel base?

They were looking in Alderaan places.

What did the cow say about the Death Star?

"That's no moooooooooon."

Who presides over space battles between rebel soldiers and Imperial officers?

The Galactic Umpire.

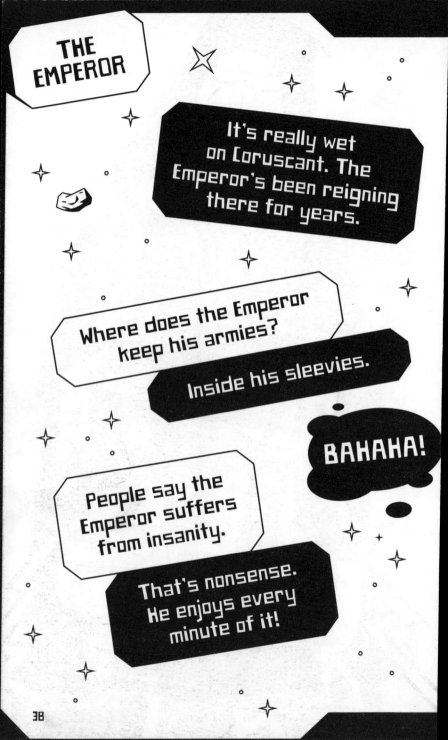

LUKE

Why did Luke ride his tauntaun to Echo Base?

It would have been too heavy to carry it.

Why did Luke join the gym?

He thought the new droids would work out.

Luke woke up not knowing which side of the desert the suns would rise from. Then they dawned on him.

AHAHA!

41

Where do rebel officers eat lunch?

Admiral Snackbar.

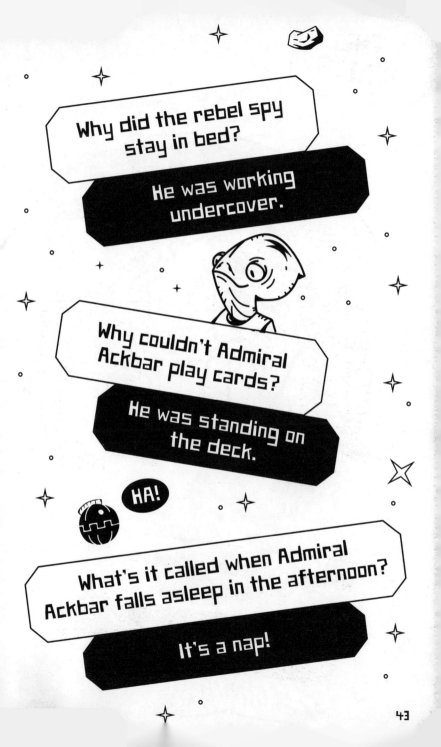

Why did the rebel spy stay in bed?

He was working undercover.

Why couldn't Admiral Ackbar play cards?

He was standing on the deck.

HA!

What's it called when Admiral Ackbar falls asleep in the afternoon?

It's a nap!

What's the temperature inside a tauntaun?

Luke warm.

Where do you take a sick tauntaun?

To a Hoth-pital.

Hilarious!

What did the wampa say to the tauntaun?

"Well, it's been nice gnawing you."

45

What is an opee sea killer's favourite food?

fish and ships.

Why are scalefish so well educated?

They swim in schools.

JABBA

Jabba's on a seafood diet. He sees food, he eats it.

What time is it when Jabba sits on your electrobinoculars?

Time to get new electrobinoculars!

What is Jabba the Hutt's middle name?

'The'.

What weighs two tons and sticks to the roof of your mouth?

A peanut butter and Jabba sandwich.

IMPRESSIVE

What did Jabba say when his enemy ran away?

I'll get you next slime!

MODAL NODES

Why did Grand Moff Tarkin get kicked out of the band?

He kept asking where the treble bass was.

How do you make a bandstand?

Take away their chairs.

HA!

Why did Figrin D'an climb a ladder?

He wanted to hit the high notes!

What's the name of the Modal Nodes' comeback album?

Revenge of the Bith.

What is a Jedi's favourite food?

Obi-Flan-Kenobi.

Who tries too hard to be a Jedi?

Obi-Wannabe.

Which Jedi Master is the most well travelled?

Globi-wan Kenobi.

ALIENS

What sort of alien is 3 metres tall, with six arms, a poison stinger and a bad temper?

I don't know either, but there's one standing behind you.

What do you call an alien with one leg shorter than the other?

Eileen.

What do you call an alien with no eyes?

Alen.

HAHAHA!

Zuckuss is pretty funny looking. He has to buy two tickets when he goes to the zoo - one to get in, one to get out!

What happened when the Gamorrean fell through the trapdoor?

They had to call a hambulance.

How do Gamorreans write
secret messages?

With invisible oink.

What do you call a
Gamorrean with no legs?

A ground-hog.

Why couldn't the
Gamorrean join the play?

He was a ham actor.

AHAHAHA!

LANDO

Did you hear the one about Cloud City? Never mind, it'd be over your head.

Why is it called Cloud City?

Because there's no Lando.

59

Which side of Chewbacca is the hairiest?

The outside!

Knock Knock!

Who's there?

Interrupting Wookiee.

Interr—

GRAUGGHAAH!!

WOOKIEES

Why did the Wookiee cross the road?

It was the chicken's day off.

What do you give a sick Wookiee?

Plenty of room!

Why are Wookiees difficult to eat?

They're too Chewie.

62

63

What do starship pilots like to read?

Comet books.

What is a light-year?

It's like a regular year, except with less calories.

HA!

How can you tell if a Star Destroyer is on its way to a party?

It's wearing a TIE.

Did you hear the one about the magic X-wing?

It flew past the planet and turned into an asteroid field.

Why are Imperial pilots fed up with space battles?

Because they always end up in a TIE.

Did you hear about the red starship that crashed into the blue starship?

The crews were marooned.

HAHA!

What do you call a starship with a broken air conditioner?

A frying saucer.

How much do space pirates pay for earrings?

A buccaneer.

Greedo built a wooden speeder bike. Wooden seats, wooden engine, wooden everything. It wooden go.

What do you call a Jawa on an iceberg?

Lost.

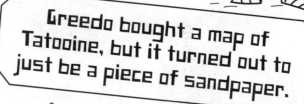

Greedo bought a map of Tatooine, but it turned out to just be a piece of sandpaper.

Did you hear about the queues at the Jawa hospital? You have to be a little patient.

LEIA

Why does Leia always know what Luke bought her for Christmas?

Because she can always sense her brother's presents!

Who does Princess Leia's hair?

Darth Braider.

How does Leia get her brother's attention?

Luke over here!

HA!

Why doesn't Leia like to eat at restaurants on asteroids?

There's no atmosphere.

REY

Did you know Rey is reading a book about Force levitation?

She can't put it down.

How do you listen to music on the *Millennium Falcon*?

On the Rey-dio.

FINN

Knock Knock!

Who's there?

Finn.

Finn who?

Finnk I better run, the first Order's coming!

Rey: What vehicle can you drive with ease?

Finn: A speeder.

Rey: Is there anything you can drive with more ease?

Finn: A speeeeeeeeeder.

Why did finn not give up?

Because he was a 'trooper.

When did finn quit his job at the restaurant?

After the first Order.

75

KYLO REN

How does Kylo like his coffee?

On the dark side.

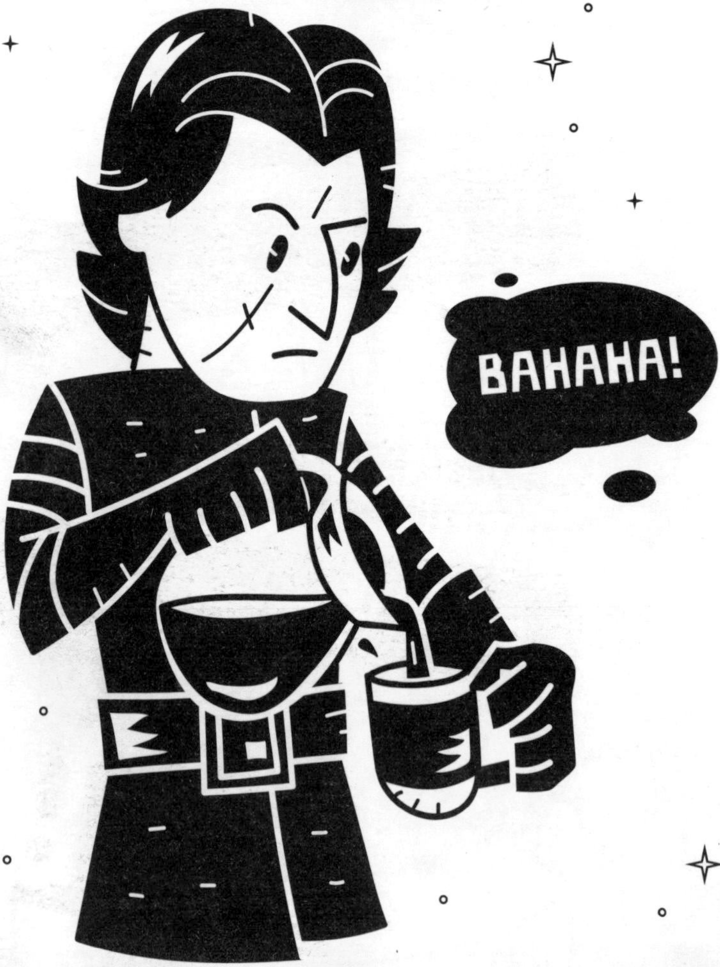

What's got wings and a lightsaber?

Kylo Wren.

Why did the chicken cross the road?

To get away from Kylo Hen.

What does Kylo Ren serve at a dinner party?

First hors d'oeuvres.

THE FIRST ORDER

First Order scientists have invented a way to walk through walls. It's called a 'door'.

What's the First Order's favourite game?

Snokes and Ladders.

What musical instrument do they play in the First Order?

The Starkiller Bass!

BB-8

Is your droid hungry?

No, BB-Ate.

Why can't you get rid of BB-8?

Because he's always a-round!

HEHE!

Why did BB-8 quit
the football team?

People kept thinking
he was the ball!

What do you call a droid that's
never on time?

BB-late.

What did Poe teach everyone at the Christmas party?

The Resisdance.

What do you say to Admiral Ackbar when he's being slow?

C'mon Calamari!

What do the Resistance and aquariums have in common?

They both have Reys and Finns!

What do Finn and Poe like to do at the gym?

Resistance training.

Why did C-3PO need to go back to school?

He was getting a bit rusty.

Why was C-3PO never lonely?

Anakin was good at making new friends for him.

What is gold and shiny, and gold and shiny, and gold and shiny?

C-3PO stuck in a revolving door!

PORGS

Why are porgs always sneezing?

They live on the planet Ahch-Toooo!

Why did the porg cross the road?

To prove it wasn't chicken.

What is brown and white and brown and white and brown and white and brown and white?

A porg rolling down a hill.

What do you call Chewbacca's half bird, half droid pet?

Cy-porg.

What is ME-8D9's
favourite type of music?

Shock and roll.

Why was Maz's castle so cosy?

It was full of snugglers.

Why did the smugglers
enjoy the musicians
playing in Maz's castle?

They have a soft spot
for the banned.

Where did Max Rebo leave his keys?

In his organ.

HAHA!

What does a baby Twi'lek wear when eating dinner?

A Bib Fortuna.

Jakku

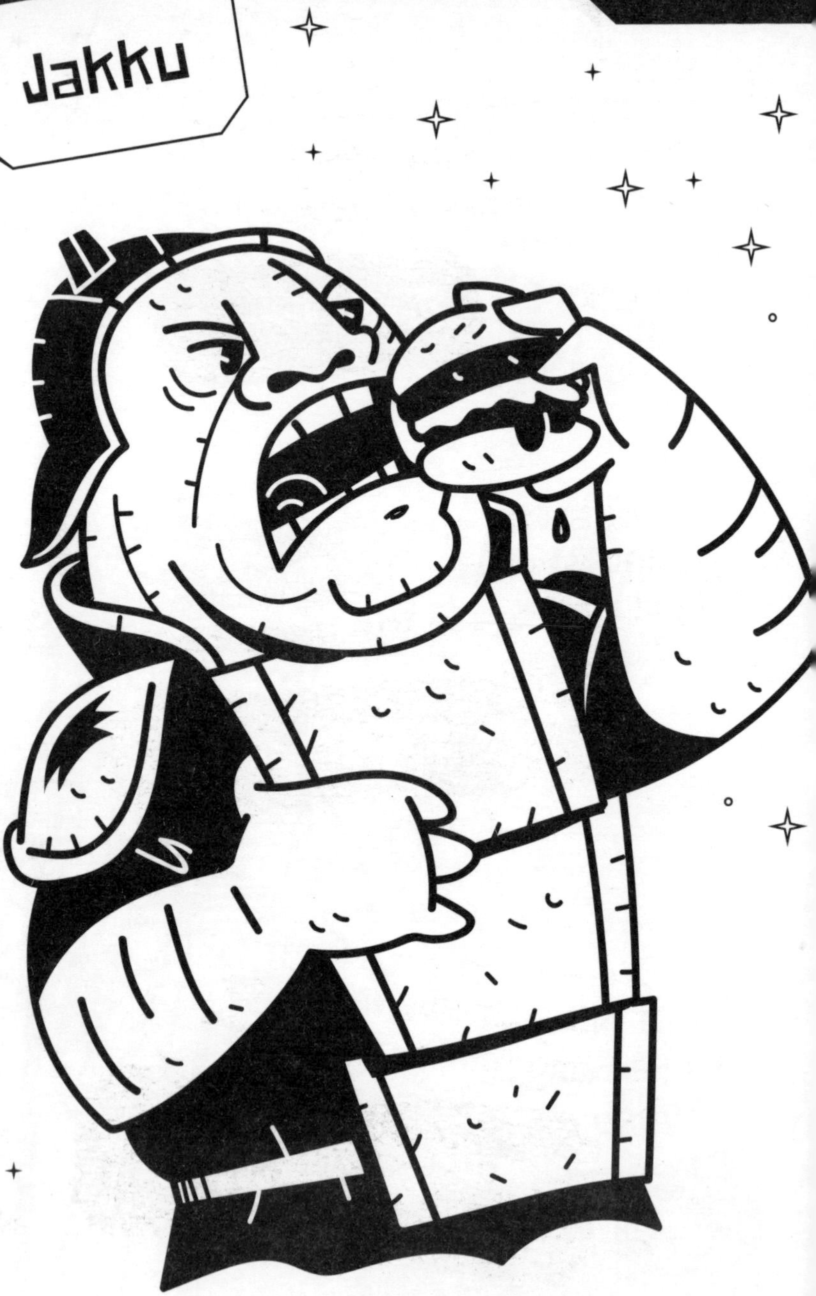

What does
Unkar Plutt eat?

Junk food!

What did the scavenger
say when she found water
in 3 places in the desert?

Well, well, well.

Why do you never go
hungry in the desert?

Because of all the sand
which is there.

X-WING SQUADRONS

How do you wash an X-wing?

Fly through a meteor shower.

Why couldn't Poe find
his sandwich?

Because BB-8 it.

What do you call an X-wing
pilot who's good at magic?

A flying sorcerer.

HEEE

What is Porkins' favourite
day of the week?

Flyday!

How do you make a dianoga laugh?

Ten-tickles!

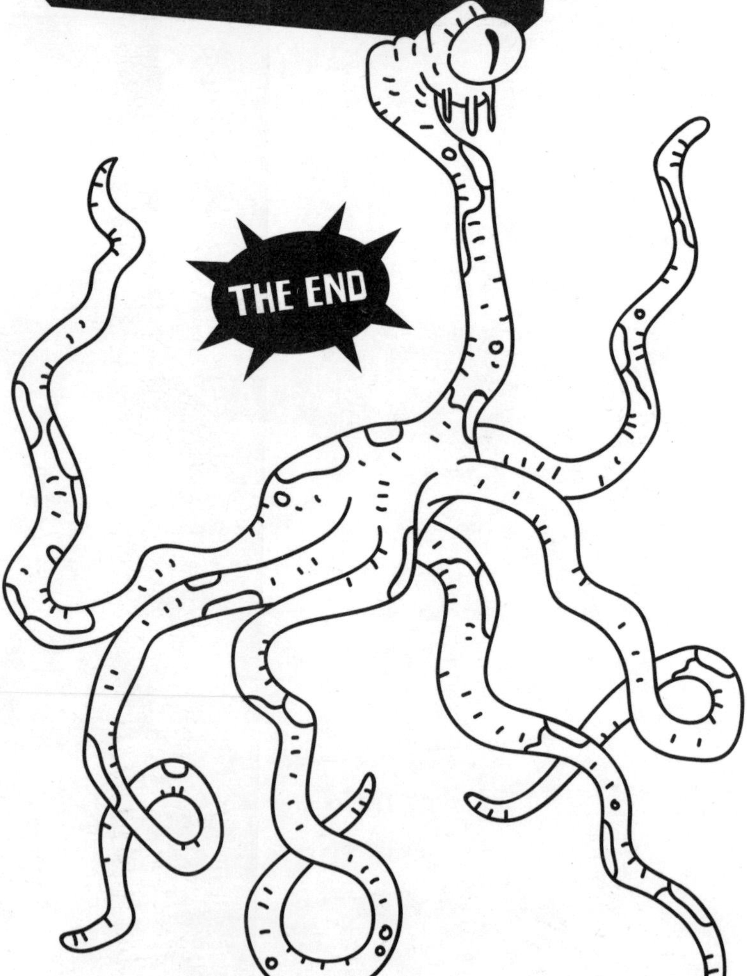

THE END